THE POLICE TACTICAL LIFE SAVER

Crucial Skills for Handling Major Medical Crises

SGT. GLENN FRENCH

43-08 162nd Street
Flushing, NY 11358
www.LooseleafLaw.com
800-647-5547

This publication is not intended to replace nor be a substitute for any official procedural material issued by your agency of employment nor other official source. Looseleaf Law Publications, Inc., the author and any associated advisors have made all possible efforts to ensure the accuracy and thoroughness of the information provided herein but accept no liability whatsoever for injury, legal action or other adverse results following the application or adoption of the information contained in this book.

©2012 Looseleaf Law Publications, Inc. All rights reserved. No part of this book may be reproduced, stored in a retrieval system, or transcribed, in any form or by any means, electronic, mechanical, photocopying, recording, or otherwise, without the prior written permission of the Copyright Owner. For such permission, contact Looseleaf Law Publications, Inc., 43-08 162nd Street, Flushing, NY 11358, (800) 647-5547, www.LooseleafLaw.com.

Library of Congress Cataloging-in-Publication Data

French, Glenn.
   The police tactical life saver : crucial skills for handling major medical crises / Glenn French.
      p. ; cm.
   Includes index.
   ISBN 978-1-60885-037-2
   I. Title.
   [DNLM: 1. Emergency Treatment--methods. 2. Military Medicine--methods. 3.   Military Personnel--education. 4. Police--education. 5. Wounds and Injuries--therapy. WB 105]
   LC classification not assigned
   616.02'5092--dc23
                                                         2011026181

All photos are the property of
Tactical Life Saver, LLC

Cover by *Sans Serif,* Saline, Michigan

Table of Contents

Dedication

This book is dedicated to my wife Rebecca Ann. Her devotion to me and my children have allowed our family to flourish.

Acknowledgment

I would like to thank *Simulaids*
for allowing me the use of their products.

About the Author

Sgt. French is a 20-year police veteran with the Sterling Heights Police Department (metro Detroit). He currently is assigned to the Special Response Team and serves as the Team Commander. He is responsible for the deployment of his personnel at tactical SWAT operations and their training. His other duties include supervising the SHPD training division. He also serves as an adjunct instructor at the Oakland Police Academy's advanced training section where he developed and instructs their Basic SWAT Course, Basic Sniper Course, Winter Sniper workshop and Active Shooter Response. Glenn is also president of Tactical Life Saver.org, a tactical training company serving the Great Lakes and Midwest.

During his tenure on one of metropolitan Detroit's County SWAT teams, he was responsible for the deployment of his personnel at tactical SWAT operations and their training. Also, Sgt. French started the "explosive breaching" program in 1998. During that time, his SWAT team was the only tactical team in the Detroit area to utilize explosives for entries. Since that time, he has had numerous explosive breaches in real-world SWAT operations.

He is a regular columnist for *Police One* and his column is the "SWAT Operator" and for the *Special Forces Newsletter* and the column is the "Blue Warrior." He serves on the review committee for the Valor Project and is committed to the development of Combat Casualty Care for Law Enforcement.

Glenn holds certifications in many tactical areas, which include: Advanced tactical SWAT command, Advanced Police Sniper, Advanced Explosive Breaching, Police Sniper, Sniper Instructor, F.B.I. Sniper Course, Hostage Rescue, CQB, Tactical Firearms, Threat Assessments, Tactical Leadership, Barricaded Gunman, Advanced Combat Shooting, Explosive Handling, Bomb & I.E.D. Recognition, Terrorist Bombers, Advanced Precision Driving, Deliberate & Dynamic Building Entries, Explosive Entries and Tactics, Rapid Deployment, Multiple Terrorist training tactics, Tactical Operations in Haz-Mat environments, Response to WMD Incidents Instructor, Police

Response to Active Shooters, WMD Terrorism Response and many others.

As a Detective, he was successful in investigating and prosecuting homicide, armed robberies, organized crime and various other cases. Prior to his assignment to the Criminal Investigation Unit, he was a crime scene technician where he gained valuable knowledge processing major crime scenes such as homicides, suicides, fatal accidents and many others. While serving on the crime scene unit, Sgt. French was recognized as the ISIS "Officer of the year" for the state of Michigan for work he had done on a serial armed robbery case involving numerous agencies.

During his military tenure in the U.S. Army, Sgt. French gained valuable experience in CQB, infantry tactics and explosive breaching operations. The military experience molded his character and instilled in him an esprit de corps attitude, which is the foundation of his leadership today.

Introduction

Tactical Lifesaver (TLS)

In 1997, Los Angeles police officers responded to an active shooter incident in North Hollywood. The incident lasted 39 minutes and resulted in seven civilians and eleven officers being shot and injured. The suspects shot 1,100 rounds from fully automatic AK-47s, fully automatic Bushmaster .223s and a .308 H&K semi auto. Aside from having trouble neutralizing their adversaries, officers were unable to get emergency medical support and paramedics to the injured officers and citizens inside the hot zone. For those 39 minutes several officers and civilians were trapped with no medical attention. The officers that suffered injuries were unable to treat themselves and had to rely on other officers to make daring rescues at the expense of their own lives to save them and get them to advanced medical care.

In this type of situation most EMS personnel won't deploy to render aid in an unsecured environment such as a "hot zone." This leaves the potential for an untreated injury to quickly become fatal. A simple laceration that causes massive hemorrhage on a thigh can bleed out very quickly. An untreated chest wound from a gunshot or knife could become critical or develop into "tension pneumothorax." An unconscious officer involved in an auto accident on a back country road may suffer an airway obstruction from facial injuries and become fatal before EMS arrives. These injuries are critical and can potentially become fatal if left untreated for more than five minutes.

The good news is these injuries can be treated in the battle space by the officer himself or any responding officer with "Tactical Lifesaver" training. A study conducted of officers from one municipal agency and one sheriff's department concluded that 32% of officers reported a line of duty injury serious enough to require emergency room evaluation. 41% reported they had responded to the scene of a seriously injured officer and, most importantly, 70% of these officers were on scene prior to

1

prehospital care. None of these officers except one had any formal training on how to treat the injuries described earlier. Tactical lifesaver training can provide these officers with the skills and equipment needed to treat and possibly save another officer's life or maybe their own.

Tactical Lifesaver (TLS) training isn't new to the military. The hard lessons learned from battlefield healthcare appeared in a 1996 issue of "Military Medicine." Previously, military guidelines for trauma management used tactics from the civilian sector. The new concepts originated from the Special Operations Command; the new tactics outlined in 1996 were collectively referred to as Tactical Combat Casualty Care (TCCC).

TCCC was based on historical wounding patterns in combat, which also are relevant to police officers and SWAT cops who share many operational parallels with their military counterparts.

We in law enforcement have the benefit of the quick response from EMS and trauma hospitals near our tactical operations. So we don't share the same disadvantage as the soldiers on the battlefield. However, in this era of mass murder and active shooters (Ft. Hood; Ogden, Utah; Omaha, Nebraska; Virginia Tech; Columbine, etc.), it's not hard to imagine that you or your partner(s) could be involved in an incident where you're cut off from EMS after sustaining a life-threatening injury while responding to an active shooter incident. That's when your Tactical Lifesaver tactics may save you or your partner's life.

Tactical Lifesaver training can be utilized to prevent many deaths that are common to law enforcement. Tactical Lifesaver skills can prevent officers' deaths in every aspect of what we do. Injuries sustained in a high-speed chase in a rural environment resulting in a traffic accident, a gunshot wound sustained to the leg while responding to a domestic call where the officer remains pinned down from his adversary, or a blunt trauma injury such as a knife wound sustained in the throat while fighting on a traffic stop are all potentially fatal injuries if not treated within five or less minutes. This book provides you with a guide of the necessary skills to aid in the prevention of officers' unnecessary deaths. It's important that this book not be the sole source of training for the TLS but be used in conjunction with credible Tactical Combat Casualty Care Training courses and hands-on practical training scenarios.

The single most contributing cause of police officers deaths in the United States is gunshot trauma. That being said, keep in mind that most gunshot trauma sustained in combat by military forces have less than five minutes to be stabilized from life-threatening injuries. After the first five minutes pass your chances of survival significantly decrease.

Consider this: In the North Hollywood bank robbery several officers sustained gunshot wounds and those officers spent the next 30 minutes calling for medical assistance. These men took on their adversary and fought to stay alive without medical treatment for a significant amount of time. Any officer subjected to this type of call can greatly benefit from Tactical Lifesaver training and equipping themselves with the proper tools to stay alive.

In a nine-year period from 1998–2007 the FBI Uniformed Crime Report of the Law Enforcement Officers Killed and Assaulted program (LEOKA) study indicates that 533 officers died from "felonious assault." Of these deaths, 198 sustained head trauma injuries and 90 officers sustained chest trauma injuries. The head trauma and chest trauma were the largest two groups of injuries that caused death to these warriors. The data indicate that 123 of these deaths were potentially preventable with the immediate intervention of Tactical Lifesaving skill sets when applying the military data of percentages on preventable deaths.

These numbers and statistics for the most part represent the average law enforcement officer responding to everyday patrol calls for service and encounters on the street such as traffic stops. Therefore it's easy to surmise that any officer at anytime can encounter a life-threatening injury requiring immediate medical treatment. You could be a sheriff's deputy working in a large county, a state trooper working a long stretch of highway or in a small town working the midnight shift alone and if you call for help your backup and EMS may be five, ten, or fifteen minutes away.

If officers face this dilemma of prehospital care and backup assistance being so far off, then Tactical Lifesaver skills should be just as important to you as the swat officer in a city agency. Let's face it: You could be assaulted on a traffic stop or at a domestic call, miles from any assistance. A gunshot to the femoral artery can potentially bleed out well before your backup or EMS arrives.

Currently, statistics in the United States are not focused on collecting data from police officers' deaths as it pertains to preventable deaths; however, our military counterparts have been researching this topic since the Vietnam War. Some of their data in Iraq and Afghanistan indicate that the widespread use of tactical combat casualty care skills are a dominate factor in reducing preventable deaths and in achieving a casualty case rate of just over 10%, which is a reduction of 36% since the Vietnam war. This has resulted in an estimated 1,000 battle-injured lives saved in Iraq and Afghanistan.

So consider this, the military data indicates 60% of all preventable deaths on the battlefield are due to severe hemor-rhage from isolated extremity trauma. That is a significant percentage of preventable deaths that could be treated by self-aid or buddy aid using hemorrhage control tactics from the Tactical Lifesaver skill sets.

You warriors must understand that a life-threatening injury can occur at anytime. No matter where you patrol if you're cut off from EMS because your laying in a hot zone bleeding out then you better have the training and equipment to save your own life, because those firemen and paramedics aren't coming into a hot zone to rescue you!

When I refer to a hot zone it could be as simple as you laying in a front yard of a house where you and your partner just approached on a domestic violence call. If your adversary ambushes you on the approach and delivers a femoral shot and you fall, unable to walk, and your adversary pins you down with potential gun fire then your buddies will surround the house. Cops are warriors and a couple of those guys are going to attempt an officer rescue. It's critical to have the ability to save your own life. In this case it may be as simple as applying a blood-clotting agent and a dressing or a one-handed combat tourniquet.

The second most common cause of preventable death in military combat is tension pneumothorax, which occurs when a collapsed lung causes pressure to build up inside the chest cavity and then compresses the heart. If this occurs shock and death may result from a very treatable injury in a short period of time. Because the LEOKA report has limited medical data, it's difficult to determine the exact number of potentially preventable deaths from chest trauma or tension pneumothorax. The data indicate that 129 officers suffered chest trauma and, in 90 of those cases, the chest trauma was the cause of death. If we assume and apply the military data and percentages of battlefield deaths to the LEOKA data, 11 of 29 of these officers may have died from a battlefield treatable injury, tension pneumothorax. This data would indicate that uniformed and tactical officers should be trained in the treatment of tension pneumothorax, and it should be a key focus for law enforcement trainers when conducting TLS training.

The TLS skill set for tension pneumothorax requires inserting a large gauge needle into the chest cavity to vent trapped air. This procedure is referred to as a needle decompression. The military has proven that this skill set saves lives on the battlefield and now teaches it to most combat soldiers. The military has also trained the entire Iraqi police force in this skill set as well as the rest of the tactical combat casualty care tactics. A recent study of tactical law enforcement officers showed that the officers could retain these skill sets for a period greater than six months.

The smallest cause of preventable death in combat is due to airway compromise. The LEOKA data indicate that injuries

5

sustained to the neck and throat were responsible for the deaths of 21 officers during the study period. Again, the LEOKA data aren't engineered for the specific collection of data as applied to combat casualty care, but airway injuries are easy to fathom. Whether they occur from a gunshot wound or from an accident during a police pursuit, an airway injury can be treated with a simple insertion of a nasopharyngeal airway tube. This simple tool can save a life when waiting for EMS to arrive, especially during an active threat or waiting for EMS or backup to arrive in a rural setting.

Military medics and EMS have been trained for decades on the concept of the "Golden Hour." This Golden Hour was thought to be the time limit soldiers must receive medical care from combat injuries to sustain life. The concept of the "Golden Hour" was invented by R. Adams Cowley, an Army surgeon and father of shock trauma medicine. The Golden Hour emphasized the importance of getting a soldier to medical care at an established medical facility as quickly as possible.

The conflicts in Iraq and Afghanistan proved to the Army medical community that, even more important than the Golden Hour, was the first 10 minutes after a traumatic injury. The first 10 minutes is now being called the "Platinum 10" by some, and is the basis for innovative new combat medic training. The Platinum 10 asserts that a critically injured soldier stabilized in the first 10 minutes of receiving his or her injury in combat has an excellent chance of survival provided the soldier makes it to definitive medical care soon thereafter. The Golden Hour focused on getting the patient to definitive surgical care within one hour but didn't properly focus on the care given in the first 10 minutes en route to the hospital.

Some in law enforcement have reduced the time to five minutes and believe that an officer who is shot may die from shock or hemorrhage, a breathing airway obstruction, or a tension pneumothorax if these causes of death aren't treated immediately.

Introduction

What this means for law enforcement is if the bleeding is not stopped, breathing re-established, and the airway properly cleared in the first 5-10 minutes the likelihood of the injuries becoming fatal are great.

The primary focus of the Platinum 10 is to stop the bleeding in the first 10 minutes. The temporary use of a tourniquet to manage life-threatening extremity bleeding is recommended. This principle is supported by the wealth of Vietnam combat casualty data indicating injuries from blood loss due to extremity injuries represented the number one etiology of preventable battlefield deaths.

Research also indicates that if a shooting victim is alive when medical treatment arrives that he most likely will survive. This is the foremost reason that every law enforcement officer should be trained in Tactical Lifesaver skills.

Critical components of tactical combat care will train the officer to assess the tactical situation and the victim needing aid, for example, most penetrating gunshot wounds to the head are fatal. So, if an officer is in an active shooter situation and he locates a civilian victim with a penetrating gunshot wound to the head, he may assess the tactical situation from cover and make a logical determination if he should risk exposure to gunfire or not to render aid to the victim whom most likely is already dead. Remember: An officer's primary duty is to stop the criminal behavior and the secondary duty is to render aid. Tactical combat care training is designed to provide skills to an officer so that he may render lifesaving aid while remaining in the fight. This training will not turn officers into medics, but it may allow an officer to stabilize an injured warrior until paramedics arrive and can render advanced aid. Approaching a victim in a tactical formation is another vital component of the TLS skill set. Although most swat teams train on this tactic, uniformed officers typically do not, which places them at a significant disadvantage. There are many other important nuances in the initial phase of assessment and approach tactics that officers will be trained to recognize and mitigate.

Basic first aid training is another component and will refresh the officer's basic first aid training in areas like airway and breathing treatment and hemorrhage and shock treatment. These topics will be taught in greater detail than what they typically receive but it will include performing the skills in a combat environment. The most significant component of this training will include lifesaving skills that are not basic first aid skills but techniques used by medical personnel that may be necessary to save your victim's life in a combat situation where medical personnel aren't available to render advanced support.

One skill that officers will be trained to use is the naso-pharyngeal airway tube. This flexible tube can maintain an open airway in a victim until medical personnel arrive so you can stay in the fight.

Treating tension pneumothorax is another life-threatening injury officers should be trained to deal with. Tension pneumo-thorax is a condition that occurs when a bullet or shrapnel penetrates a lung. The air from the lung enters the chest cavity and fills the space between the ribs and the lung. When this happens the lung no longer has the space needed to inflate. Therefore, the lung may collapse and the heart can be shifted, causing blood flow to stop to the heart. Performing a chest decompression with a large gauge catheter can stop tension pneumothorax from occurring and provide immediate relief, thus saving the casualty from death.

Massive blood loss (hemorrhage) is another life-threatening injury that can be prevented. Officers should be trained in the use of blood-clotting agents and the use of tourniquets. These simple-to-use tools can stop massive blood loss and save lives. Although tourniquets may cause the loss of a limb, losing a limb is better than losing your life. Training in tourniquet application in a combat environment is a critical component in the combat care training. Modern tourniquets make the process simple and fast.

The last component for the TLS is the "Warrior" mindset and how it applies to the officer's survival during combat.

Here is a simple thought that I like to live by:

"The way to Warrior Supremacy is through preparation and training; the way to failure and defeat is through arrogance and indifference."

Preparing the Warrior Spirit begins with confidence; confidence is built through training. This book will provide the TLS with valuable lifesaving skills that may save an officer's life.

The goal of the tactical lifesaver concept is to improve the survivability of accidental and non-accidental life-threatening injuries encountered by swat operators in the field and uniformed officers on patrol. This concept is not designed to turn officers into medics, but rather to teach the time-critical skills that may permit survival long enough for victims to obtain critical advanced medical care.

The Tactical Casualty Combat Care concept has become the standard of care for the tactical management of combat casualties within the Department of Defense and is the sole standard of care endorsed by both the American College of Surgeons and the National Association of Emergency Medical Technicians for casualty management in tactical environments. The objective is to give the operators the ability to stabilize life-threatening bleeding and airway issues that present during a tactical combat environment.

The lifesaving tactics in this book should only be used in the most critical situations. It is always preferable to seek medical aid from TEMS, EMS, Fire and Paramedic personnel before using these lifesaving techniques. However, if you find yourself in a combat environment and a fellow officer has been critically injured and TEMS, EMS, Fire or Paramedic personnel will not enter the hot zone to render aid, or you are cut off from their care and the casualty may die from injuries if he/she isn't treated immediately, and the casualty can't be immediately evacuated then you may choose to use these lifesaving techniques to save a life. This is the Tactical Lifesaver.

Goals of the Tactical Lifesaver

Tactical Combat Casualty Care guidelines are the framework and foundation for combat trauma training within the Military Special Operations Command. The concept was implemented more than 10 years ago and was recently updated when it became apparent that civilian prehospital medical care models, including advanced trauma life support, basic trauma life support and advanced cardiac life support, were unsatisfactory models for providing care during combat missions.

In 1993, the Naval Special Warfare Command began researching combat associated deaths due to penetrating trauma. This study was later assumed by the United States Special Operations Command and their results were published in a supplement to "Military Medicine" in 1996 (Butler, F.K. Jr., 1996). The findings from this study became the foundation for a combat trauma curriculum intended to combine critical medical care with good small unit tactics within the military with hopes of reducing casualties in combat. The first course was taught by the Navy Bureau of Medicine and Surgery in 1996 during the Undersea Medical Officer's Course and was later adopted by the Navy SEALs.

This course has been tested during combat operations, updated periodically, and now represents the best practices for providing care during combat missions in the military. This course is now taught to soldiers throughout the Department of Defense. These lifesaving skills have become a normal part of combat training for military soldiers. It's time for law enforcement to adopt this concept as we do with so many other military tactics. We train for combat on a regular basis and on occasion we face combat on the streets. Consider this, on average 58,000 police officers are assaulted each year resulting in approximately 16,000 injuries. If you fall victim to this statistic you will now have the ability to possibly save yourself or a fellow officer with the use of tactical lifesaver tactics.

If you're still not convinced that law enforcement doesn't need this skill set consider this: During conventional ground

11

combat operations 85% of deaths result from catastrophic wounds. It's unfortunate, but no modern medical care can save these soldiers. However, military tactical combat casualty care directs medical resources to care for the remaining 15% of injured soldiers, who, when treated aggressively, will survive their wounds. Furthermore, 60% of preventable deaths result from extremity hemorrhage treatable by a tourniquet or direct pressure. Lastly, 33% of preventable deaths are caused from tension pneumothorax or penetrating chest trauma, and 6% of preventable deaths are from maxillofacial trauma causing airway obstruction.

Advances in medical care, personal and vehicular armor, changing tactics, and the widespread use of improvised explosive devices by opposition forces in Iraq and Afghanistan are changing these numbers slightly.

The vast majority of potentially survivable deaths due to injuries sustained in combat remain extremity and compressible hemorrhage, readily controllable with tourniquets, direct pressure and hemostatic agents. The lessons learned in the military tactical combat casualty care remain valid and prove to be successful. The application of these skill sets provided during active combat operations incorporate good small unit tactics to minimize the risk of incurring additional casualties, and initial lifesaving care requires a small number of simple interventions and requires minimal equipment.

We in law enforcement can all benefit from the Tactical Lifesaver training. So many officers assume this skill set is solely for tactical operations, however. It's my opinion that the uniformed officer can apply these techniques on a more frequent basis. It's not uncommon for a sheriff's deputy or state trooper to be or more minutes away from ambulance personnel or a fire rescue squad as they patrol the outskirts of their counties. If they suffer a severe laceration or amputation in a car accident you may be their only chance for survival. Critical injuries such as severe hemorrhage, tension pneumothorax, and airway blockage can cause death in a short amount of time when left untreated.

Goals of the Tactical Lifesaver

The goal of the Tactical Lifesaver is to train, equip, and prepare the uniformed officer for lifesaving skills that a large number of officers don't currently have that will undoubtedly save lives.

Priorities of the Tactical Lifesaver

Priorities

When responding to critical incidents such as an active shooter, conducting swat operations, or any other situation in which the TLS is called to duty, the TLS must lawfully maintain these three priorities:

1. Save preventable deaths

2. Prevent additional casualties

3. Complete the mission

These three priorities are critical to the mission's success. The TLS must stay focused on the mission's objective during a critical incident. Losing your "situational awareness" will greatly diminish your ability to focus on all three priorities.

Management of situational awareness will greatly enhance your ability to make good tactical decisions inside the battle space.

Tactical Lifesavers must recognize two particularly important principles:

1. To perform the correct intervention at the correct time during combat.

2. A medically correct intervention performed at the wrong time in combat may lead to further casualties.

It is imperative to the safety of the TLS that he or she conducts a proper assessment of the potential victim and a proper assessment of the scene. If a rescue team conducts an extraction from a hot zone where one of the rescuers are critically injured and the victim is already dead then this attempt to save a dead man's life may have cost the life of another.

The "officer rescue" reflects the fundamental conflict between a need to do what is perceived as correct for the injured officer versus the risk such action creates, both to the rescuers and to the injured officer. Is the risk worth the benefit? Logic would state that risks and benefits should be weighed in order to come to a reasonable decision as to whether or not to attempt a rescue. The most appropriate tactical medical care may actually be threat neutralization.

Outfitting the Tactical Lifesaver

The following commercial medical supplies are crucial for the officer to have available and the TLS be trained in its use. These products are widely available and are relatively inexpensive. These items can be carried in several configurations. A small pouch can be useful and placed on a swat operator's vest or the items can be carried in a back pack.

Patrol officers can carry the same pouch in a "tactical response bag." A tactical response bag can be a simple pouch or small backpack that slings over your shoulders when responding to critical incidents. The bag should have extra ammunition for your primary and secondary weapons, a couple bottles of water, energy bars, and some pain relief medication. Most importantly for the TLS it should contain, at a minimum, the following supplies:

- Chest Seal (Asherman, Bolin, Rusch, Hyfin and others)

- Nasopharyngeal Airway (Rusch and others)

- Catheter (BD Angiocath™ Auto guard™, ARS from North American Rescue)

- Tourniquet (C-A-T™ and MAT one handed)

- Hemostat (CELOX™, Quickclot, CitoFlex, Hemcom and others)

- Black Rubber Trauma Gloves

Figure 4-1.
Tactical Medical Kit

- Emergency Trauma Dressing (2) 6"

- Rolled Gauze (2) 4.5"x 4 yards

17

- Nylon Pouch or Tactical Response Bag

- Rescue tether

Remote Assessment Operations

Conducting a remote assessment in a tactical operation may be the single most critical component of the skill sets used by the TLS. An assessment not properly conducted could cost you your life or further injuries to the victim.

Any officer involved in rescuing an injured officer can tell you that the raw emotion(s) that are felt while attempting a rescue can be overwhelming. In the grand scheme of policing, dealing with a shot or injured officer may become the most important operation of your career. When you plan the operation it's important not to let your cognitive thinking process become negatively influenced by a desperate feeling of hopelessness. Your actions must be calculated and concise. If not, you may injure more officers that are tasked with the operation and ultimately leave your victim at the mercy of your adversary. You must revert back to your training when this occurs and engage the warrior spirit, maintain your situational awareness, and trust your tactics to lead the rescue operation to success.

Your first objective is to evaluate the status of the injured officer. Do this from a point of cover or concealment. Use binoculars and night vision devices to detect signs of life. If necessary clear your weapon, providing you're in a safe zone and use the optics mounted on it to get a better view of the casualty. Detect for any signs of life by looking for a rising chest or any movement that may indicate the officer is alive. Keep in mind that the injured officer may be laying still so that he doesn't draw any further attention or gunfire to himself. If that's the case try to verbalize with the casualty and simply ask about his condition. If no movement or signs of life are detected and you conclude the officer is fatally injured then do not attempt a rescue until the threat has been neutralized.

With signs of life, there are several options for the TLS. Try to verbally communicate with the injured officer and direct him to move to your position or to cover. If he can move to cover then direct him to do self-aid until the threat is neutralized. An injured officer may be able to apply a tourniquet, blood-clotting agents or a pressure bandage in some cases. The situation may require you to provide instruction in the proper steps of self-aid due to his diminished mentation.

If your assessment dictates that an immediate rescue is necessary, identify where your threat will come from as you conduct the operation. You must conduct a remote assessment of the hot zone from a position of cover or concealment. Your planning will need to take into account the use of cover and concealment for your tactical approach. Improvised explosive devices are another concern when making your approach.

The use of smoke in the kill zone when making your approach from the last point of cover can provide significant concealment for the movement. Proper tactics are that you move from the last point of cover to the victim and then back to the next point of cover, quickly. As most tactical officers are aware, your rescue team should not move any quicker than they can effectively engage their adversary. Otherwise your adversary will create havoc on the entire operation.

A smooth pace is fast enough.

While moving as a rescue element you must be able to effectively engage your adversary when he decides to engage you. Therefore a fast pace will not allow you to deliver precision fire support as needed.

As law enforcement officers we should shy away from "suppressive fire" while providing care under fire. We are duty bound to engage threats only as they present themselves. The tactic of suppressive fire works fine for the military; but unless your adversary poses a threat to the rescue team, I would shy away from sending bullets down range indiscriminately. However, this is a general statement. If your threat is active or if your threat is so significant that your operation is vulnerable, then fire suppression may be needed to safely conduct the operation. Remember that you must justify your actions in a report following the operation, so follow the state laws in which you work and write a concise report of the incident.

Consider your available resources to make the operation safer. If you have an armored vehicle readily available for use then it has an obvious benefit. Tactical blankets provide a wall of security for your rescue team as the team moves the injured officer. Some blankets provide protection from most pistol calibers and some rifle calibers. Combining the tactical blankets with smoke is a great tactic and will greatly enhance your success.

I like to teach swat cops to "fight chaos with chaos." With an officer rescue operation you may choose to use diversionary devices such as flash bangs, brake and rake windows, or deploy chemical munitions in your adversary's stronghold. Any of these tactics will create confusion and a delay in the processing of the OODA loop of your adversary. When this occurs you have bought your rescue team some valuable time.

If you find your adversary has chain locked himself in the target building, such as a school or commercial building that is keeping your rescue team from getting inside, then drive a patrol car up to the locked doors, slowly drive the car through the doors so the doors collapse and give you access. Once inside the building the driver of the car should position the car to provide cover and then provide security for the rescue team as they enter through the opening.

Activating the sirens and lights may also be a benefit for two reasons

First, the shooter will know your presence and your intentions and therefore, as most mass murderers do, he may commit suicide or even stop the killing so that he can take cover.

Second, innocent civilians will run to the sound of the siren providing them with a safe route.

Officer Rescue Tactics

Three Phases of Risk in Officer Rescue

The *Approach Phase* occurs during the transition from the relative safety of the point of last cover and concealment (LCC) into the "hot" zone, where a potential active threat exists. The Approach Phase consists of the distance that must be covered in order to reach the injured officer. It is during this period of time that the team first exposes itself to the potential threat.

The *Aid Phase* consists of the period of time the officers spend in the hot zone, under threat of effective fire, assessing the injured officer, and performing preliminary care. This phase is high risk in nature because your adversary is likely now aware of your presence and the rescue attempt, the rescue team is relatively static, and situational awareness is easily lost while focusing on the injured officer.

The *Extraction Phase* consists of the distance that must be covered to return the injured officer to a position of relative safety, where further medical aid and definitive evacuation can be performed.

Basic Principles

There is an inherent dilemma when deciding to conduct an officer rescue. What if the casualty is already dead? For example, you and your partner respond to the scene of a domestic violence call and as you two approach the home a man appears in the window and starts shooting at you and your partner. You return fire with your handgun as you retreat to cover behind a vehicle parked in the driveway. The shooting stops as soon as you reach cover, but you then realize your partner is laying in the front yard and he isn't responding to your attempts to speak with him.

You summon backup immediately and you still see the gunman walking around inside the small house with a rifle caliber weapon, and occasionally he will glance from behind a curtain. Your backup units arrive in short order and SWAT has

23

also been activated to respond to the scene. At this point you realize you have at least a barricaded gunman and perhaps a hostage crisis depending on what is actually transpiring in the home. One thing is for certain, it's only been a short couple of minutes and your partner is laying less than hundred feet away, possibly dying as you watch helplessly. What do you do? The raw emotions from such a tremendous amount of stress on the battlefield can be overwhelming for any individual regardless of your training and experience.

The most fundamental question is whether this situation represents an officer rescue or a body recovery. Many times it is difficult to tell whether the situation is a rescue or a recovery. You must check for signs of life and in the absence of any signs of life you must not allow your overwhelming desire to do what you perceive is necessary to recover your partner's body at the total disregard for the safety of the officers needed to make the recovery.

Due to the nature of the incident, initial hands-on assessment may be impossible. The assessment is based on the absence of signs of life. The obvious signs such as body movements, a rising chest, or the ability to speak indicate the possibility of the need for immediate lifesaving care.

If it remains impossible to distinguish between rescue and recovery, the most appropriate response is often to assume a rescue is needed and act accordingly. However, by simply taking a few seconds to make quick proper assessments of the victim rather than immediately rushing forward into a danger zone, officers conducting the rescue operation will not needlessly place themselves in danger by performing a proper risk assessment of the victim and the tactical challenges facing them.

Approach Phase

The first critical decision to be made from a tactical standpoint is determining whether the injured officer will die if an

24

officer rescue is performed or if TLS skills aren't rendered to the injured officer immediately.

Remotely assess the injured officer to determine his ability for a self-extrication or self-aid. If the victim can perform self-aid or even extract himself from the hot zone then coach him in the TLS tactics. Keep in mind that the victim's situational awareness and cognition may be diminished. Your coaching then becomes a critical component in the victim's success. Be patient and mindful of the tactical hurdles the victim is facing.

If self-aid or self-extraction isn't viable and the decision is made to conduct an officer rescue, then the TLS should survey the scene for potential threats and dangers. Scan the area for cover, concealment, threats, secondary devices, suspects, and so on. Then determine the best route for approach to the casualty and the best route of return.

Utilize all resources available to you at the time of the operation. Armored vehicles are a perfect choice for rescue operations, but it usually takes time for the vehicle to arrive. Ballistic blankets are a great choice and they offer a large area of ballistic protection. However, ballistic blankets are large and expensive, which makes their availability limited to the uniformed officer.

The ballistic shield is the most readily available tactical option for the patrol officer. These shields offer limited protection from various rounds but limited protection is better than none. Training with these shields during squad tactics and on the gun range is imperative. Don't wait until you need to protect your life with one before you train with them. They tend to be heavy and awkward, which can place an officer at a disadvantage if he or she is unfamiliar with its use.

Shields are best utilized when carried with both hands. Hold the shield high so that it offers the largest area of protection. If used properly most ballistic shields offer protection from the knees to above the head when properly carried.

Some officers like to place their weapon along the side of the shield as they make their approach. This tactic can work providing the officer is properly trained. However, shooting

25

from this unstable platform has its own nuisances that can make a successful engagement of your adversary very difficult.

If man power permits, I prefer that officers use two hands to carry the shield while concentrating on the approach. Let your cover officers provide fire protection.

Tactical Approach

Approaching an injured officer must be conducted with a tactical formation to minimize the dangerous exposure from your adversary. Tactical formations and approaches vary from agency to agency. The critical component in the choice or planning of your tactical approach needs to emphasize the safety of the officers conducting the operation.

Conducting an officer rescue operation with an active assailant can be one of the most dangerous operations any tactical team or group of uniformed officers can participate in. Losing an additional officer when conducting the rescue operation will further complicate an already complex problem.

The first step in the planning of the approach is to form a rescue team. A team of six officers is recommended; however, a single officer can perform a rescue if the circumstances require the immediate rescue of an injured officer. Keep in mind that performing any rescue operation alone is very difficult. Factors such as providing cover for the approach, providing TLS in the battle space under fire and the extraction of the injured officer will be significantly safer and may increase the chance for a successful operation with additional officers.

In a team of six officers the six rescue officers should stand paired shoulder-to-shoulder, stacked three deep. These first two officers have two main objectives to perform. First, they should carry ballistic shields or ballistic blankets to provide a limited amount of cover for the rescue team's movement. The second objective is that they will guide the actual movement of the rescue team to the injured officer and the route they take. If the first two cover officers are responsible for the movement this will enhance the team's overall safety because the situational awareness of the other rescue officers can now focus on any potential threats that may be present.

If ballistic shields and blankets aren't available to use by the rescue team then the first two officers will use their weapon systems to provide security. In other words, these two officers will have their weapons down range in a "combat or tactical ready" so they may engage an adversary immediately. If your operation requires the use of weapons as the cover for the approach, then utilizing patrol rifles or shotguns are preferred due to the ability to engage targets at greater distances than your service pistol.

When the decision is made to move out, be decisive, be tactical, and maintain a high level of situational awareness. Remember your objective is to rescue an injured not to create a larger tactical problem.

The next two officers in the rescue team will provide security from the left and right of the shield officers. These

Figure 6-1. Officer Rescue

two officers are the security element of the rescue squad. They must be in a combat ready or tactical ready position as the squad moves toward the injured officer. The security element would be better outfitted with patrol rifles or shotguns, however, hand-guns can still provide security in a hasty environment.

A unique problem to officer rescue and the security element in its ability to engage an adversary is the speed in which the rescue team moves. A tactic that is commonly overlooked in the combat space is "don't move faster than you can shoot." What this means is, if your security element is moving faster than he or she can effectively engage and neutralize an adversary then your squad is moving too fast.

27

Training is the key here for patrol officers and swat cops. It's important to train the officer rescue tactic at the gun range. Get your officers behind the ballistic shield or blanket, form your rescue squad and engage targets down range. Training this tactic on the gun range in live fire conditions will help familiarize the entire squad with live fire engagements as they move toward the injured officer. Once they are familiar with the pace they develop in live fire training they must maintain that speed in combat.

To aid in the realism of the training, utilize a training dummy as the injured officer such as the "Rescue Randy" manufactured by Simulaids of Saugerties, New York. Have the rescue squad conduct the entire TLS skill set on the range. Don't allow them to just shoot and move. When an officer is overloaded with combat stress and fatigue his cognitive thinking will automatically revert to the repetitive training that he has been exposed to in the past. By familiarizing the officers with live fire, you will make them more comfortable in a combat environment. If the officers are more comfortable in the combat environment their chances of successfully completing the mission objective increases significantly.

The last two officers will perform any necessary field care and the rescue. The first four officers should walk over or past the injured officer to provide cover and security for the extraction officers. They will now be in a forward position of the casualty, providing security for the rescue element.

Aid Phase

Now that the rescue element has passed over the casualty and have taken a position to provide security, take a few seconds to assess the medical needs of the casualty. Remember, you may be the first responder in this rescue. The burden is then placed on you to know what should and should not be done, and how to do it. What are the officer's injuries? What medical care is needed? What medical care can be safely performed?

Is there cover nearby where the officer can be moved to have this care provided, prior to extraction? How long are you willing to spend in the hot zone? By answering these questions ahead of time, exposure time in the danger zone will be minimized, therefore reducing risk.

Care under fire is the care rendered upon reaching the injured officer when the potential for active threats still exists. Due to the high threat level, medical care in the hot zone is extremely limited. Avoid any medical treatment in the hot zone and focus solely on extrication. Minimizing care in the hot zone minimizes exposure time and therefore risk.

The only suggested medical care provided in the hot zone is to control life-threatening hemorrhage. Severe hemorrhage is the only injury that the TCCC guidelines recommend that may need to be treated while standing unprotected in a hot zone. The thought is that airway management and tension pneumothorax can wait long enough to extract the casualty to medical care or cover; however, the severe loss of blood cannot wait. Therefore, you may find your rescue element placing a tourniquet or a pressure bandage on a severe laceration or amputation prior to extracting the casualty.

Figure 6-2. Care Under Fire

Due to the nature of the hot zone, the need for continued situational awareness, and the inability to provide sustained pressure on a bleeding wound in the hot zone and during rapid extraction, is achieved through the rapid use of a tourniquet. A general rule of thumb is that tourniquet placement in the hot zone should take no more than 10 seconds. Remember that during this time, the officer applying the tourniquet will

29

experience a diminished situational awareness due to his focus of providing care to the casualty.

Every officer should be instructed in the rapid use of a tourniquet; the hot zone is not the place to use any equipment for the first time. Pre-designation of the aid officer provides multiple advantages. First, that officer will have personal protective equipment like rubber gloves already on for body substance isolation. Second, the rescue aid officer will know that he/she can focus on the casualty in relative safety, as the other officers will maintain that situational awareness. Most importantly, the rescue aid officer can expedite medical care and extraction by having a medical preplan, including having the tourniquet out and readily available for use.

Extraction Phase

The goal of this phase may not be to remove the officer to a point of definitive safety. The situation may dictate that the officer is moved to a position of relative safety, provided by the availability of cover. Once in this position additional TLS care can be rendered and emphasis placed upon neutralizing the threat.

Avoid separation of the rescue unit. The extraction team consists of two groups of officers, those physically performing the extraction by carrying or supporting the injured officer and those providing protection and situational awareness. The extraction group has a tendency to outpace the cover group. When this occurs, a gap may be created and they become dangerously exposed. So, focus on the tactic and maintain a solid safe pace.

Consider the safest and alternate routes that provide cover. Avoid turning your backs to your adversary during the e x t r a c t i o n . By doing so, you may leave your flanks and rear exposed to fire.

Figure 6-3. Officer Extraction

The rescue of an injured officer is a critical lifesaving tactic. These rescues are high-risk and the key to any successful operation is appropriate, realistic, and ongoing training.

Single Officer Rescue

If the need arises to effect a single officer rescue the use of a rescue tether will aid the rescuer in the extraction of the casualty. A rescue tether can be made or purchased and is nothing more than a length of rope with a carabiner tied at each end. The tether should be a minimum of 62" long; however, the longer the better. A longer tether will allow you to tie loops in it so that you can adjust the length by simply placing the carabiner in the desired loop.

Prepare the rescue tether for operation prior to conducting the rescue. Place the tether around your waist and clip the carabiner to the rope. Pull the slack tight and place the rest of the tether in your weak hand pocket. Make your assessment of your travel

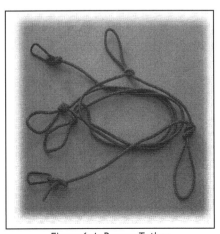

Figure 6-4. Rescue Tether

31

route, get your weapon up and move to the casualty. Once you have reached the casualty perform an assessment for aid. Consideration for moving the casualty out of the hot zone before conducting care under fire should be the priority.

Obviously getting both you and the casualty out of the hot

Figure 6-5. Casualty Drag - Feet

zone is a smart choice with no other fire support or cover available. Once you determine to make the extraction, take the rescue tether out of your pocket and move to the casualty's feet. Reach down (you may have to holster or sling your weapon) and loop the free end of the rescue tether around the casualty's feet and pull tight. You are now ready to pull the casualty out of the hot zone, feet first. Make sure you secure the casualty's weapon. Drag the casualty to a position of cover to conduct the aid phase or to a position where he or she can be evacuated for medical treatment.

A single officer rescue is not the safest choice but it may be the choice that

Figure 6-6. Casualty Drag - Vest

saves the victims life. When possible, use shields that many patrol officers carry in their squad cars. If time permits wait for back up to arrive to lend support in the rescue. A lot can go wrong with one man effecting a rescue but there are times that you won't have any other choice.

Immediate Action Plan

The rescue of an injured officer or civilian casualty is a high threat operation. The risk exists, during all phases, that the rescuers come under direct fire, and that one or more rescuers are injured. It is important that the team have an immediate action plan should this occur.

At a minimum, this immediate action plan should include:

- Suppressing incoming fire from the threat if feasible or needed.

- Identifying the presence and location of injured rescuers.

- Identifying who can continue with the primary rescue.

Immediately extract the injured rescuer, rather than retreating. When possible back-up rescue officers should be identified, not only to respond to any rescuer casualties, but also to replace the primary rescue aid officer should he/she be injured during the approach.

Figure 6-7. Tactical Approach

Situational Awareness and the Tactical Lifesaver

Situational Awareness

Understanding how to manage situational awareness while responding to patrol runs or in swat operations can greatly maximize your chances for success. Situational awareness is defined in the Army field manual as "knowledge and understanding of the current situation which promotes timely, relevant and accurate assessment of friendly, competitive and other operations within the battle space in order to facilitate decision making. An informational perspective and skill that fosters an ability to determine quickly the context and relevance of events that are unfolding."

So how does this apply to the TLS? In the context of swat operations, situational awareness refers to the unit's ability to determine the relationships of the factors, such as *perception, comprehension*, and *projection* that are present and form logical conclusions concerning any threats to the individual officer or team, and the mission objectives.

In a simpler form, situational awareness is a process our minds go through for just about everything we do. For example, when you're involved in a high-speed chase you are cognitively processing numerous pieces of active intelligence simultaneously. As the chase continues you react and act on the decisions you make from that information. This is your situational awareness in the simplest form.

Take for example a high-speed pursuit; you may process information such as:

- The info that dispatch is conveying to you over the radio about the car and suspect.

- The orders your command officers are providing over the air.

35

- Your conveyance of information relevant to the chase to the dispatch center.

- The speeds that you are chasing the suspect.

- The intersections and signals you are approaching and passing.

- Officer safety concerns and various others.

In this chase scenario your ability to process various and numerous pieces of active intelligence is your situational awareness. As you are aware from participating in or listening to these pursuits unfold some officers have a great natural ability to manage their situational awareness. It's typically obvious just by their radio brevity alone during the pursuit. However, other officers lose their cool and find it necessary to yell or scream into the radio, pass the lead chase car or even try and take over the pursuit entirely. These officers have lost control of their situational awareness and tend to make a stressful situation even worse.

If the TLS loses his ability to manage his situational awareness he can create more problems than he is already dealing with simply because he may make incorrect tactical decisions that can endanger other officers or, at a minimum, contribute other factors that now have to be mitigated as well.

Training for improved situational awareness inside the battle space

Improving the TLS situational awareness through training requires measurement of specific objectives through "decision-based live fire," "tactical operations training," and "tactical patrol response training" to identify *"objective measures"* and *"subjective measures."* The training should measure and assess cognitive situation awareness skills such as task management, information discovery and filtering, prioritization, perception, attention span, memory, and preparedness.

Objective measures can directly assess situational awareness by comparing officers' perceptions of the situation to the reality of the situation or training objective. By evaluating objective measures from the officers' perceptions of the situation and comparing them to what is actually happening. This will allow you to score or assess the accuracy of their situational awareness at a given moment in time during the training scenario. Thus, the assessment provides a direct measure of situational awareness and does not require operators to make judgments about situational knowledge on the basis of incomplete information.

Training objective measures can be gathered in one of three ways:

1. Real-time as the task is being conducted. Ask questions related to the training objective in real-time, during the task without stopping.

2. During an interruption of the training. Stop and ask questions about the task.

3. After the training objective is complete, conduct a critique of the performance.

Subjective measures directly assess situational awareness by asking individual officers to rate their own situational awareness or by the observed situational awareness from other individuals watching the officer in the training scenario. Subjective measures of situational awareness are relatively straightforward and simple to conduct. However, several limitations should be noted. Individuals making subjective assessments of their own situational awareness are often unaware of information they do not know.

37

Self-ratings may be useful because they can provide an assessment of the TLS degree of confidence in their situational awareness and their own performance. Measuring how situational awareness is perceived by the TLS may provide information as important as the TLS actual situational awareness. Over confidence or lack thereof in situational awareness may have just as harmful an effect on an individual's or a team's decision-making as errors in their actual situational awareness.

Subjective critiques of an individual's situational awareness may also be made by experienced observers such as peers, commanders, or outside experts. These observer critiques may be superior to self-ratings of situational awareness because they have more information about the true state of the training scenario, objective, and environment than the operator who is performing the objective.

When an officer encounters a situation that offers multiple cues as to its meaning and consequences, those that are relevant to our accessible concepts tend to be noticed more easily, and the situation tends to be interpreted in terms of that concept rather than another one. Basically, we observe things in a manner in which we desire to observe them. The officers situational awareness, depends on knowledge, motives, emotional state, experiences, expectations, fatigue and other physical factors, and other variables.

Swat operators with a keen sense of situational awareness have the ability to put their "game face" on prior to any operation. This holds true for uniformed officers responding to high-risk patrol runs. This process of putting your game face on is actually an individual's ability to heightening his or her senses and alertness to the task at hand. Some operators may mentally rehearse their individual roles in the operation. Some may listen to music on the way to the scene and others can simply transition at a moment's notice.

Once you're in this heightened sense of situational awareness you will have the ability to pick up on other variables and bits of intelligence that you may have missed otherwise. When conducting training you will witness this first hand as you observe the TLS work through his training objective. However, keep in mind that the reinforcement from the objective and subjective measures must remain positive to be effective. When in training we all make mistakes, and some officers mistakes create negative emotions that can interfere with learning but also lead to withdrawal. Some officers become anxious at the thought of doing any training at which they may be viewed as failing. Teaching situational awareness can increase the officer's performance and confidence.

The key to success is to *slow* the officer's response to a speed where he can process the information, *prioritize* the information and then *act* decisively. Once the officer develops this skill even his perception of slowing the decision-making process actually becomes faster.

Imagine yourself involved in the high-speed pursuit as mentioned earlier, and you have all those active bits of information to process as the pursuit ensues. Officers must prioritize each bit and then process it. When he processes each bit, he must rely on training, experience, and what his instincts tell him is the correct course of action. Then he must not hesitate to act on his decisions. Sometimes not making a decision or choosing a course of action can be worse than making the wrong decision.

Through training you can achieve optimum situational awareness. Take any training objective and introduce stress and multiple problems at once for that objective. When you introduce those problems, provide several potential options to solve them. Identify the *objective* and *subjective measures* and create the critiques and questions for the officers' measures. Give the officers a short period of time and force them to make decisions based on the information that you provided. Afterward critique their performance and discuss all of their options. Remember to keep it positive!

Then continue this style of training and make it very repetitive. Repetition in training develops memory. Memory fosters confidence, decisiveness, and speed for making decision in combat. Once this training becomes repetitive to your officers then you have helped them develop confidence in the face of adversity. This is when you have achieved a high level of *situational awareness.*

Cognitive Thinking in Combat Environments

Cognitive thinking may be the single most important ability an officer dealing with a deadly adversary in that dark moment of combat can possess. Your success may hinge on your cognitive thinking abilities.

The cognitive thinking process includes:

- *Divided attention and your ability to manage it:* Divided attention allows you to handle two or more tasks at one time.

- *Working memory and your ability to utilize it under pressure:* Working memory is the ability to retain information for short periods of time while processing or using it.

- *Processing speed of the information presented to you:* Processing speed is the rate at which the brain handles information.

- *Long-term memory of past incidents and training:* Long-term memory is the ability to both store and recall information for later use.

- *Visual processing of the situation:* Visual processing is the ability to perceive, analyze, and think in visual images. Visual discrimination is seeing differences in size, color, shape, distance, and the orientation of objects. Visualization is creating mental images.

- *Auditory processing of the situation:* Auditory processing is the ability to perceive, analyze, and conceptualize what is heard. Auditory discrimination is hearing differences in sounds, including volume, pitch and duration.

- *Logic and reasoning of the information and situation:* Logic and reasoning skills are the abilities to reason, prioritize, and plan.

Tactical lifesavers should focus on these cognitive thinking skills to quicken and more effectively respond to an adversary's actions. Creating training with realism is the primary factor that will help build better cognitive thinking skills so when you are subjected to actual combat you will feel that you've already been there and been exposed to that environment.

Introducing stress into all of your training is paramount. There are several techniques you can use when training Tactical Life Savers to achieve this. Stress can be as simple as running in full police or tactical gear prior to engaging targets on the gun range, or performing officer rescues in full duty gear while being timed on the task. These are some simple ideas and obviously the list can go on and on and you're only limited to your imagination in dreaming up different stress techniques. The key to introducing stress into your Tactical Life Saver training is to make it applicable to what the training objective is and make sure you take you and your officers to that dark, uncomfortable place, over and over again.

Simunition scenarios are another great technique. Training on Tactical Lifesaver tactics using simunition provides stress while conducting the training operation. The mere presence of the possibility you may be shot by simunition induces stress. Simunition (reduced energy, non-lethal marking cartridge) induces stress on two levels. First is the fear of the sting when you're shot but most importantly, officers do not want the stigma of being "the guy that got tagged" by his adversary, it's embarrassing. This is the time a lot of officers throw their tactics out the window and it's a great time to capitalize on training points, as you will now have a captive audience. Processing speed, auditory perception, and divided attention are the focus of simunition scenarios.

The best leaders in combat tend to be motivators who can give instruction under perilous conditions, so try this technique to build leadership skills and induce stress for those who lack in leadership skills. Pick different team leaders for the day during training sessions, including less experienced officers and have them plan and lead an officer rescue. During the training day, throw challenging tasks at them that will incorporate some type of physical stress, with a deadline to complete the challenge and make the challenge some type of officer rescue or tactical life saver problem.

Incorporating a physical challenge into your training can be very simple. For example, take your six-person rescue team and have them compete against other rescue teams by pushing a police car up a hill for time. After they get to the finish line, ask the team pertinent questions about rendering tactical lifesaver aid such as signs and symptoms, proper procedures for a chest decompression, and so on. This is great for team and confidence building, but when you add the tactical lifesaver tactics, they will be forced to use logic and reasoning under a great deal of stress from the competition and the physical aspect that was performed. On the gun range have the rescue teams matched up in head-to-head competition, running and traversing obstacles while engaging targets and conducting officer rescue drills. Range safety is paramount but head-to-head competition splits their attention and they will train their auditory processing and visual processing skills while trying to move without endangering the other team's shooters. As the rescue team leaders command their team they will experience all of the above cognitive thinking processes and improve their cognitive thinking. The focus of this training is logic and reasoning as well as divided attention.

Observation training known by some as a KIMS game is another great technique that improves cognitive thinking skills. Give your officers a simulated scout mission with the objective to perform a threat assessment of a hot zone by setting up a large room in a commercial building, a school gymnasium or an

43

outside hot zone. Set the scene by placing items that are natural to that environment, items foreign to that environment and things that can be critical pieces of intelligence to factor during the rescue operation. Try to overload the objective with items to be observed, so much so that it will be impossible to note everything. Give the rescue team a predetermined amount of time (a minute and thirty seconds is a good starting point) to observe the hot zone, assess the scene, gather intelligence, and report back with the information they collected.

When they conclude the operation evaluate the information they collected. The focus to this training is to hone the memory and the visual processing of the information which is critical in mission planning. The key component to training for cognitive thinking is repetition and intensity. You should strive to replicate the fear of the battle, the intensity, the uncertainty, the chaos, and the ambiguity of combat and repeat it over and over again until you and your officer's cognitive thinking process is sharp and ready to conduct rescue operations.

Training the Tactical Lifesaver

Training

Training the Tactical Lifesaver is as important as rendering care to an injured officer.

There are three components in training the Tactical Lifesaver:

1. Classroom and lecture.

2. Practical Exercises.

3. Testing.

These components are a minimum of training that is acceptable for the Tactical Lifesaver. Proficiency is paramount when training these lifesaver tactics. Classroom lecture should equal no less than four hours to deliver the curriculum. Power points will deliver your message with ease.

Lecturing the officers in these core TCCC skills can develop a thorough knowledge base:

Remote Assessment

1. Identifying threats

2. Conducting a Remote Assessment

3. Victim Color Codes

4. Signs to Look For

5. Rescue vs. Recovery

6. Cover and Concealment

7. Safe Approach

8. Communication

Airway and Breathing

1. Airway Blockage

2. Field CPR

3. Nasopharyngeal Airway

4. Chest Decompression

Hemorrhage and Shock

1. Hemorrhage Treatment

2. Respirations, Pulse, and Mentation

3. Tourniquets

4. Blood-Clotting Agents

5. Shock Prevention

6. Moving the Victim

Lifesaving Skills

1. Nasopharyngeal Airway insertion

2. Identifying Visible Signs of Tension Pneumothorax

3. Treating Tension Pneumothorax with a Chest Decompression

4. Application of Blood-Clotting Agents

5. Application of a Tourniquet

Practical exercises and scenario training is just as important as classroom lecture. However, this may also be the most effective means of delivering the skills. As with most law enforcement training, you will have a captive audience when it comes to the hands on portion of these tactics. Capitalize on this opportunity by requiring each student to participate. These exercises should be evaluated and graded for proficiency.

The following tactics need to be conducted through practical exercise:

- Conduct a site survey of the hot zone

- Remote assessment of the victim

- Care under fire operations

- Officer rescue operations

- Care under cover

- Evacuation operations

Three Stages of Care

There are three stages of care that the tactical lifesaver must concern him/her self with. It's critical to understand these stages before planning a rescue attempt.

- *Care Under Fire:* is the care rendered by the rescue officer to the injured officer while still under the threat of hostile fire. Fire superiority is a key element under this phase.

47

Injured officers may need to assist in returning fire if they have the capacity. Controlling hemorrhage should be the only care rendered during this phase. Airway management shouldn't be a consideration at this point until the officer is moved to safety.

- *Tactical Field Care:* is the care rendered once you're no longer under the threat of hostile fire. The available medical equipment is that carried into the field by the officer.

- *Combat Casualty Evacuation:* is the care rendered by advanced medical personnel in a safe zone.

Airway Management

In military combat, 6% of preventable deaths occur from airway obstructions. Although this is the lowest percentage of fatal injuries, it may be the easiest to render aid for. If you discover an unconscious officer in a hot zone and his airway is obstructed, simply inserting a nasopharyngeal airway may prevent a fatality. This procedure is simple and quick to perform. It should be noted, however, that if the victim is still under the threat of fire move the victim to a position of cover or a place of relative safety.

The time it takes to move the victim outweighs the need to unblock the airway.

Airway Management in an unconscious casualty without airway obstruction:

- Chin lift or jaw thrust maneuver

- Nasopharyngeal airway

- Place casualty in the recovery position

Airway Management in a casualty with airway obstruction or impending airway obstruction:

- Chin lift or jaw thrust maneuver

- Nasopharyngeal airway

- Allow casualty to assume any position that best protects the airway, include sitting

- Place unconscious casualty in the recovery position.

Inserting Nasopharyngeal Airway

A nasopharyngeal airway is a tube that provides an open airway and helps to keep the tongue from falling to the back of the mouth and blocking the airway. Do not use the nasopharyngeal airway if the roof of the casualty's mouth is fractured or brain matter is exposed. Also do not use the nasopharyngeal airway if there is clear fluid coming from the ears or nose. This may indicate a skull fracture.

1. Place the casualty on his back with his face up.

2. Lubricate the tube with water or sterile lubricating jelly.

3. Insert the airway.

    a. Expose the opening of the casualty's nostril.

    b. Insert the tip of the airway tube into the nostril.

Position the tube so that the bevel (pointed end) of the airway faces toward the septum (the partition inside the nose that separates the nostrils).

Insert the airway into the nostril and advance it until the flange rests against the nostril.

Lubricate the naso-pharyngeal airway tube with sterile lubricating jelly.

Figure 10-1. Naso Lube

50

Insert the nasophary-ngeal airway tube.

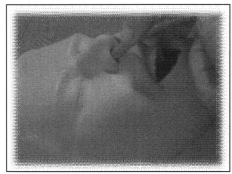

Figure 10-2. Naso Insert

The nasopharyngeal airway tube inserted.

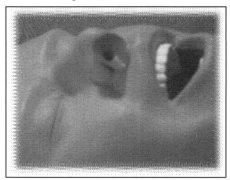

Figure 10-3. Naso Inserted

Never force the airway into the casualty's nostril. If resistance is met, pull the tube out and attempt to insert it in the other nostril. Place the casualty in the recovery position.

Recovery Position: The recovery position allows blood and mucus to drain out of the casualty's nose and mouth and not to drain back into the airway. To place a casualty in the recovery position:

1. Roll the casualty as a single unit onto his side.

2. Place the hand of the casualty's lower arm under his chin.

3. Flex the casualty's upper leg.

51

Continue to monitor the casualty's breathing. If the casualty does not have a nasopharyngeal airway inserted and his breathing rate falls below two breaths every 15 seconds, insert a nasopharyngeal airway. If tension Pneumothorax develops, perform a needle chest decompression.

Note: Remember major trauma is a surgical problem and the casualty needs medical attention as soon as possible. Advanced medical care and immediate extraction and evacuation to a Level One Trauma Center are critical.

Penetrating Chest Trauma & Tension Pneumothorax

The body has two lungs. Each lung is enclosed in a separate airtight area within the chest. If an object punctures the chest wall and allows air to get into one of these areas, the lung within that area begins to collapse. In order for both lungs to collapse, both sides of the chest would have to be punctured. Any degree of collapse, however, interferes with the casualty's ability to breathe and reduces the amount of oxygen available for the body to use.

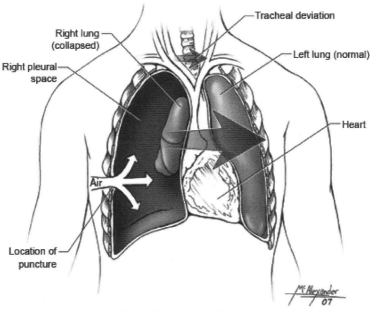

Figure 10-4. Tension Pneumo
Illustration by Jason M. McAlexander, MFA.
Courtesy Wild Iris Medical Education, Inc.
wildirismedical.com

Sucking Chest Wound

Injuries can occur to an officer when a bullet or a piece of shrapnel rips open a hole in the chest wall, entering the lung, and causing it to collapse. The victim gasps for air, has extreme difficulty breathing and frothy blood often bubbles from the wound. This is what is known as a sucking chest wound. If not recognized properly and treated promptly, the victim may die.

What occurs is the chest cavity is no longer a sealed system and unrestricted air is allowed to rush through the wound in the chest wall and into the chest cavity during inhalation. This now-positive intrathoracic pressure system causes the lung on the affected side to collapse. Unless the hole in the chest wall is patched the lung is unable to re-expand.

The untreated collapsed lung results in lack of oxygen in the blood and rapidly leads to loss of consciousness and coma. When this pressure kinks off the large blood vessels returning all of the body's blood to the heart, it results in decreased blood flow to the heart. After a few minutes the heart no longer pumps enough oxygenated blood and the body goes into irreversible shock and the victim can die.

The term "sucking chest wound" comes from the audible motion of air into but not out of the pleural cavity, which causes an eventual tension pneumothorax. Sucking chest wounds require an immediate occlusive dressing.

The chest seal is an effective method in treating this type of wound.

1. Begin by clearly exposing the wound and preparing the area for an occlusive dressing.

2. If possible, have a second Swat operator assist and, with a gloved hand, cover the wound while you prepare or improvise the dressing. If there is no assistant and the

victim is conscious, place the victim's hand over the wound.

3. Cover the wound with a chest seal or your improvised occlusive dressing. Intubation may be required at this point, even if the patient is conscious, especially if the victim's condition deteriorates.

Open Chest Wound

If an operator's chest wall is penetrated by a bullet, knife blade, shrapnel, or other object it may cause an open chest wound. If you are not sure if the wound has penetrated the chest wall completely, treat the wound as though it were an open chest wound.

Some of the signs and symptoms of an open chest wound are:

- Sucking or hissing sounds coming from the chest wound.

- Casualty coughing up blood.

- Frothy blood coming from the chest wound. The air going in and out of an open chest wound causes bubbles in the blood coming from the wound.

- Shortness of breath or difficulty in breathing.

- Chest not rising normally when the casualty inhales. The casualty may have several fractured ribs.

- Pain in the shoulder or chest area that increases with breathing.

55

- Bluish tint of lips, inside of mouth, fingertips, or nail beds. This color change is caused by the decreased amount of oxygen in the blood.

- Signs of shock such as a rapid and weak heartbeat.

Check for both entry and exit wounds. Look for a pool of blood under the casualty's back and use your hand to feel for wounds.

- If there is more than one open chest wound, treat the more serious, largest, heaviest bleeding wound first and then treat what appears to be the smaller wound.

- If there is more than one wound to a side, such as an entrance and exit wound, apply the flutter valve seal to the wound on the casualty's front and a full seal (all four sides taped down) to the wound on the casualty's back.

- Expose the area around the open chest wound by removing, cutting, or tearing the clothing covering the wound. If clothing is stuck to the wound, do not try to remove the stuck clothing as this may cause additional pain and injury. Cut or tear around the stuck clothing. Do not try to clean the wound or remove objects from the wound.

Since air can pass through dressings and bandages, you must seal the open chest wound with plastic, cellophane, or other nonporous, airtight material to prevent air from entering the chest and collapsing the lung. The wrapper from an emergency bandage or a field first aid dressing can be used. Foil or material cut from a poncho or the like can also be used.

If possible, use supplies from the casualty's first aid kit rather than your own. You may need your supplies in case you have to administer aid to yourself later.

- Prepare the sealing material. Cut the airtight material as needed so that it lies flat and will extend at least two inches beyond the edges of the wound all directions.

- Have the casualty exhale (breathe out) and hold his or her breath. This forces some of the air out of the chest wound. The more air that can be forced out of the chest before the wound is sealed, the better the casualty will be able to breathe after the wound is sealed.

The casualty should resume normal breathing after the wound is sealed. If the casualty is unconscious or cannot hold his or her breath, place the sealing material over the wound after his chest falls but before it rises.

Apply and Tape the Airtight Material Over Wound:

- Place the cleanest side of the sealing material directly over the wound. If a plastic bandage wrapper is being used, place the inside surface of the wrapper the side without printing, directly over the wound.

- Check the material to make sure that it extends at least two inches beyond the wound edges in all directions. If the material does not have a two-inch margin, it may not form an airtight seal and may even be sucked into the wound. If the sealing material is not large enough or is torn, remove it and obtain other airtight material to form the seal.

- Tape down three edges of the material, usually the top edge and two side edges. This creates a "flutter valve" effect. When the casualty inhales, the plastic is sucked against the wound and air cannot enter the wound. When the casualty exhales, air may be able to exit the wound through the untapped, bottom edge of the plastic.

57

Commercial emergency medical chest seal

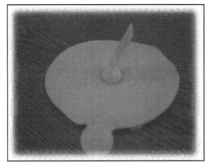

Figure 11-1. Chest Seal

Remove the backing from the adhesive chest seal

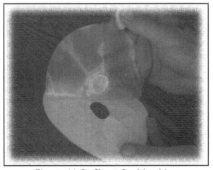

Figure 11-2. Chest Seal backing

Apply the chest seal to the casualty

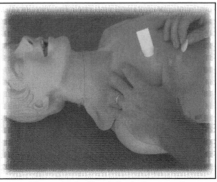

Figure 11-3. Chest Seal placement

Chest seal placed on the casualty. Note the one way valve is located over the wound.

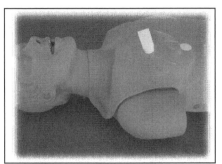

Figure 11-4. Chest Seal applied

If there are two wounds affecting the same lung, apply airtight material to the back wound and tape down all four sides so that air cannot enter or escape.

Dress the Wound. Apply an emergency bandage. The dressing and bandage will help to protect the airtight material from damage and provide pressure to the wound.

- Place the dressing pad directly over the plastic wrapper forming the flutter valve and secure the dressing with the bandage. The bandage should not be applied so tight that it interferes with the casualty's breathing.

- If the casualty is able, you can have him or her hold the dressing pad in place while you apply the bandage. If he or she cannot help, then you must hold the dressing in place while securing it.

- If an object is protruding from the chest wound, do not try to remove it. Place airtight material around the object to form as airtight a seal as possible. Stabilize the object by placing a bulky dressing made from the cleanest material available around the object. Apply improvised

59

bandages to hold the sealing material and dressings in place. Do not wrap the bandages around the protruding object.

Recovery Position

Place the victim in the recovery position or evacuate for medical treatment. To place a casualty in the recovery position:

- Roll the casualty as a single unit onto his or her side.

- Place the hand of the casualty's lower arm under his or her chin.

- Flex the casualty's upper leg.

Treating Tension Pneumothorax

Tension pneumothorax occurs when there is a buildup of air in the pleural space that cannot escape. If the air pressure outside the lung continues to increase, the affected lung may continue to collapse. In addition to causing further collapse of the affected lung, the increasing air pressure pushes the mass of material, including the heart that separates the two pleural sacs in the opposite direction. This movement may compress the uninjured lung, major blood vessels, and the heart and can cause the heart to stop functioning. A needle chest decompression may relieve the pressure.

On the battlefield it is believed that tension pneumothorax from a penetrating wound to the chest will cause approximately one-third of preventable combat associated deaths. A needle decompression of the chest is a skill that patrol officers and SWAT operators can be taught and should be prepared to use.

Recent studies measuring chest wall thickness have shown that the catheter used to decompress a chest should be at least 3.25 inches (8 cm). In a study of 110 patients admitted to a

Level 1 trauma center, computerized tomography (CT) scanning measured the chest wall thickness of the second intercostal space in the mid-clavicular line to be 4.5 cm (+/- 1.5 cm) on the right, and 4.1 cm (+/- 1.4 cm) on the left. 50% of patients in this study had a chest wall thickness measuring over 4.4 cm (1.75 in). These authors concluded that among a general civilian population, a standard 5 cm (2-inch) angiocatheter would likely be unsuccessful at reaching the pleural space in 50% of patients.

In a similar study of patients who may better represent the law enforcement special operations community, CT scanning was used in 100 male military personnel to measure the chest wall thickness at the second intercostal space in the mid-clavicular line.

The mean perpendicular thickness was 4.86 cm (SD 1.10 cm). As expected, the chest wall thickness of these men was greater than the general civilian population. These authors concluded that an 8 cm angiocatheter would have reached the pleural space in 99% of subjects.

Signs and Symptoms of Tension Pneumothorax

Signs and symptoms of tension pneumothorax include the following:

1. Anxiety, agitation, and apprehension.

2. Diminished or absent breath sounds.

3. Increasing difficulty in breathing (dyspnea) with cyanosis (bluish tint of lips, inside of mouth, fingertips, and/or nail beds)

4. Rapid, shallow breathing (tachypnea).

5. Distended neck veins.

61

6. Abnormally low blood pressure (hypotension) evidenced by a loss of radial pulse (pulse at the wrist).

7. Cool, clammy skin.

8. Decreased level of consciousness.

9. Visible deterioration.

10. Loss of consciousness.

11. Tracheal deviation (a shift of the windpipe to the right or left).

These signs and symptoms may be difficult to assess in a combat environment. You should consider tension pneumothorax exists when:

1. The casualty has an open chest wound and

2. The casualty is having increasing respiratory difficulty.

Needle Chest Decompression

If an officer suffers with progressive respiratory distress and known or suspected torso trauma, then you may consider a tension pneumothorax and decompress the chest on the side of the injury with a 14-gauge, 3.25 inch needle/catheter inserted in the second intercostal space at the midclavicular line. Ensure that the needle entry into the chest is not medial to the nipple line and is not directed toward the heart.

CAUTION: A needle chest decompression is performed ONLY if the casualty has a penetrating wound to the chest and serious increasing trouble breathing.

Treat all open and/or sucking chest wounds by immediately applying an occlusive material to cover the wound and securing it in place. Monitor the casualty for the potential development of a subsequent tension pneumothorax.

Inserting a Catheter/Needle

Prepare Catheter/Needle Unit. Remove the catheter/needle unit from its packaging and then remove the protective covering.

1. *Insert the Catheter/Needle.* Firmly insert the needle (with catheter covering) into the skin above the top of the third rib into the second intercostal space at a 90-degree angle. Continue inserting the needle until the chest cavity has been penetrated. You will feel a "pop" as the needle enters the chest cavity. A hiss of escaping air under pressure should be heard.

2. **CAUTION:** Proper positioning of the needle is essential to avoid damaging blood vessels and nerves that run along the bottom of each rib.

3. *Withdraw the needle* from inside the catheter while holding the catheter hub to keep the catheter in place. The catheter will remain as a means for air trapped in the chest to escape to the atmosphere.

4. *Secure the Catheter.* Use a strip of tape to secure the catheter hub to the chest wall.

Monitor the Casualty. By allowing trapped air to escape from the plural area, the casualty's respirations should quickly improve. Applying airtight material over the wound and having a catheter release trapped air permits the affected lung to re-inflate somewhat. If possible, monitor the casualty until you can provide medical care or until the casualty is evacuated to the

63

nearest medical facility. Be prepared to take measures to treat for shock.

Transport Casualty. If you have performed a needle chest decompression on a casualty with a tension pneumothorax, he should be transported injured side up rather than injured side down in order to allow access to the catheter during transport. The casualty may also be transported in a sitting-up position if the casualty finds that position more comfortable.

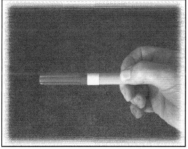

Figure 11-5. Catheter

There are simple products on the market for today's TLS designed to make this procedure easy. This system provides rigidity needed in puncturing the chest wall. When it is removed, the flexible catheter remains to allow air to escape the air pocket that is causing the tension pneumothorax.

Locate the Insertion Site. The insertion site is located in the second intercostal space (the area between the second and third ribs, counting from the top) at the mid-clavicular line (an imaginary line perpendicular to the ribs approximately in line with the casualty's nipple) on the same side of the chest as the penetrating wound.

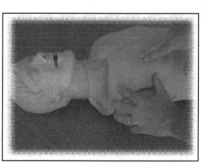

Figure 11-6. Locating Insertion Site

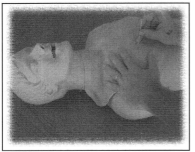

Figure 11-7. Inserting Catheter

Insert the Catheter/Needle. Firmly insert the needle (with catheter covering) into the skin above the top of the third rib into the second intercostal space at a 90-degree angle.

Continue inserting the needle until the chest cavity has been penetrated. You will feel a "pop" as the needle enters the chest cavity. A hiss of escaping air under pressure should be heard.

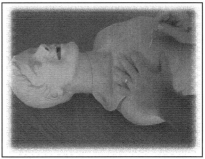

Figure 11-8. Catheter enters chest cavity

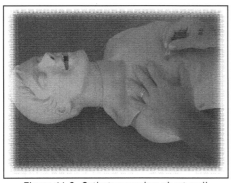

Figure 11-9. Catheter reaches chest wall

Insert the needle until the base of the catheter reaches the chest wall.

65

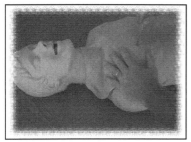

Figure 11-10. Needle removal from catheter

Withdraw the Needle. Withdraw the needle from inside the catheter while holding the catheter hub to keep the catheter in place. The catheter will remain as a means for air trapped in the chest to escape to the atmosphere. Secure the Catheter. Use the strip of tape to secure the catheter hub to the chest wall.

Here is the needle fully withdrawn and the catheter in place.

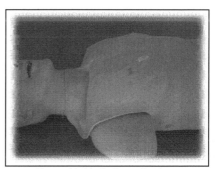

Figure 11-11. Catheter in place

66

Controlling Hemorrhage and Bleeding

Controlling Bleeding & Hemorrhage

The leading prevent-
able cause of death on the
battlefield is bleeding from
an extremity. Bleeding
(hemorrhaging) from an
extremity can usually be
controlled by applying an
emergency bandage, by
applying manual pressure
and elevating the injured
limb, by applying pressure

Figure 12-1. Wound Hemorrhage

to pressure points, and by applying tourniquets. If bleeding from
an extremity is not controlled, shock could result. Hypovolemic
(low blood volume) shock can result in the casualty's death.

Preparing the Wound

When possible put on protective gloves found in the casualty's
first aid kit or from your own. The gloves will help to protect you
from the casualty's
fluids and also to help
reduce the contami-
nation of the casualty's
wounds. Monitor the
casualty's respirations,
especially if he is un-
conscious. If the
casualty stops breath-
ing, administer mouth-
to-mouth or mouth-
to-nose resuscitation.

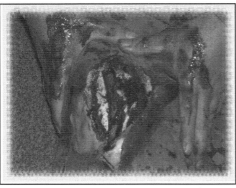

Figure 12-2. Open Wound - Mass Hemorrhage

Examine the casualty and expose the wound by gently pushing or cutting away loose clothing around the wound site. This will enable you to better view the extent of the injury. If clothing is stuck to the wound, do not try to remove the clothing. Cut or tear the clothing, if possible, so that the stuck

Figure 12-3. Expose the Wound

material remains undisturbed. If there is debris in the wound, do not try to remove it from the wound.

Check for entrance and exit wounds by examining the casualty to determine if there is more than one wound. A projectile may have entered at one point and exited at another point. The exit wound is usually larger than the entrance wound. If there is an entrance wound and an exit wound, both wounds need to be treated. Apply hemostatic agent as out-

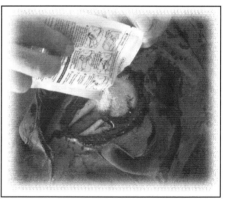

Figure 12-4. Apply clotting agent

lined in Chapter 13. If a projectile penetrates and lodges in the body, do not attempt to remove the object or probe the wound. If there is an object extending from (impaled in) the wound, do not remove the object. Apply improvised bulky dressing material made from the cleanest material available to build up the area around the object. This will stabilize the object and help prevent further injury. Apply a bandage over the bulky materials to hold them in place.

Controlling Hemorrhage and Bleeding

For compressible hemorrhage not amenable to tourniquet use or as an adjunct to tourniquet removal (if evacuation time is anticipated to be longer than two hours), use a commercial combat gauze as the hemostatic agent of choice. Combat gauze should be applied with at least three minutes of direct pressure.

Applying an Emergency Bandage

The emergency bandage can be used on any bleeding wound. It can be used both as a field dressing and as a pressure dressing. The emergency bandage consists of a sterile white pad with an elastic bandage and a pressure device used to control the amount of pressure applied to the wound. Use the following procedures when applying the emergency bandage to a wound on the casualty's extremity.

Emergency Bandage Application

Remove the emergency bandage from the casualty's first aid kit.

Figure 12-5 Prep bandage site

69

Remove the emergency bandage from the packaging and prepare it for use.

Figure 12-6. Place pad on wound

Place the pad (dressing) on the wound. Wrap the elastic bandage around the wounded extremity.

Insert the elastic bandage completely into the pressure bar. Pull the elastic bandage back over the top of the pressure bar, forcing the bar down onto the pad. Wrap the elastic bandage tightly over the pressure bar.

Figure 12-8. Secure bandage

Secure the hooking end of the closing bar into the elastic bandage.

Check the blood circulation below the bandage. The bandage should be tight enough to secure the dressing pad in place and place some pressure on the wound; however, it should not be tight enough to stop all blood circulation below the bandage.

Figure 12-8. Secure bandage

If there is no pulse, loosen the bandage and reapply. Then recheck the circulation. If the skin below the bandage becomes cool to the touch, bluish, or numb, the bandage may be too tight and interfering with circulation. Loosen the bandage and reapply. Then recheck the circulation. If loosening the

Figure 12-9.
Check bandage for circulation

bandage does not restore blood circulation to the part, the casualty should be evacuated as soon as possible.

Applying Pressure to Pressure Points

Applying digital pressure to "pressure points" is another method of controlling bleeding. This method uses pressure from the fingers, thumbs, the heel of the hand, or the knee to press at the site where a main artery supplying the wounded area lies near the skin surface or over bone. This pressure can reduce the flow of blood from the heart to the wound. It is used in combination with pressure and elevation.

Arm: Digital pressure is used to control severe bleeding of the lower part of the arm. The pressure point is located above the elbow on the inside of the arm in the groove between the muscles. Using your fingers or thumb, apply pressure to the inside of the arm over the bone.

Groin: Digital pressure is used to control severe bleeding of the thigh and lower leg. The pressure point is located on the front, center part of the crease in the groin. Using the heel of your hand or your knee, apply pressure to press the artery against the bone. Lean forward to apply pressure.

Any bleeding site not previously controlled should now be addressed. Only the absolute minimum of clothing should be removed.

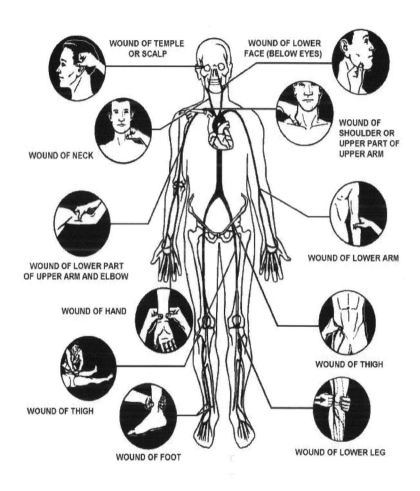

Figure 12-10. Pressure Points of the Body

Hemostatic Agents

Blood-clotting agents were originally developed to assist military medics with some of the worst wounds imaginable. Commercial blood-clotting agents have been used in the Afghanistan and Iraq wars with great success saving many lives. These products can stop fatal femoral artery bleeding within 3 minutes with compression. Also the product can stop minor bleeding in seconds. These products when mixed with a massive amount of excess blood, forms a gel-like clot in 30 seconds.

They work by bonding with red blood cells and gelling with fluids to produce a sticky clot. This clot sticks to moist tissue and plugs the bleeding site.

Applying Hemostatic Agents

- Hold the foil over-pouch so that instructions can be read. Identify unsealed edges at the top of the over-pouch. Peel open over-pouch by pulling the unsealed edges apart.

- Trap dressing between bottom foil and non-absorbable green/black polyester backing with your hand and thumb.

- Hold dressing by the non-absorbable polyester backing and discard the foil over-pouch. Hands must be dry to prevent dressing from sticking to hands.

- Place the light-colored sponge portion of the dressing directly to the wound area with the most severe bleeding. Apply pressure for 2 minutes or until the dressing adheres and bleeding stops. Once applied and in contact with the blood and other fluids, the dressing cannot be repositioned.

- A new dressing should be applied to other exposed bleeding sites. Each new dressing must be in contact with tissue where bleeding is heaviest. Care must be taken to avoid contact with the patient's eyes.

- If dressing is not effective in stopping bleeding after 4 minutes, remove original and apply a new dressing. Additional dressings cannot be applied over ineffective dressing.

- Apply a battle dressing/bandage to secure hemostatic dressing in place. Hemostatic dressings should only be removed by responsible persons after evacuation to the next level of care.

Tourniquet Use in Combat

Tourniquets

Wounds on an extremity bleeding from a major artery of the thigh, lower leg, or arm and bleeding from multiple arteries may prove to be beyond control by the methods discussed previously in this lesson. If the pressure dressing under firm hand pressure becomes soaked with blood and the wound continues to bleed, you may need to apply a tourniquet.

A tourniquet is a constricting band placed around an extremity to stop arterial bleeding by stopping blood circulation to the part of the limb below the tourniquet. Always use a CoTCCC-recommended tourniquet to control life-threatening external hemorrhage that is anatomically amenable to tourniquet application or for any traumatic amputation. These commercial tourniquets are widely available in the medical supply field. The tourniquet is applied above the wound high on the extremity, over the uniform and tighten to stop arterial bleeding or until distal pulse is lost.

In the past it was believed that the tourniquet would further damage an injured limb. However, the tourniquet's use and its ability to increase survival in casualties sustaining combat-associated major limb trauma is well established and concerns that their widespread use may cause additional injury is unsubstantiated.

Normally, a tourniquet is only used on an arm or leg where there is a danger of the casualty bleeding to death. However, if the tactical situation does not allow the time or safety for conventional methods of controlling the bleeding, a tourniquet may be applied to a bleeding wound until the casualty can be moved to safety. Once you and the casualty have reached safety, consider loosening the tourniquet but do not remove it.

A person whose arm or leg has been amputated may not be bleeding when first discovered, but a tourniquet should be applied anyway. This absence of bleeding is due to the body's normal defenses (contraction and clotting of blood vessels) as a result of the amputation. However, bleeding will start when the blood vessels relax or if the clot is knocked loose by moving the casualty.

Applying a Tourniquet

Figure 14-1. Amputated Leg

The use of a commercial tourniquet is fast and simple to use.

Figure 14-2. Amputated Leg

Remove the tourniquet from the casualty's first aid kit. Remove the tourniquet from its protective cover. Most are packaged in a one-handed configuration. Slide the wounded extremity through the loop of the self-adhering band.

Position the tourniquet two inches above the wound. If the wound is below the knee or elbow, initially position the tourniquet band two inches above the wound. If a tourniquet applied below the knee or elbow is not successful at stopping the bleeding, apply a

Figure 12-3. Position the Tourniquet

second tourniquet two inches above the joint (knee or elbow). Do not remove the first tourniquet until the second tourniquet has been applied. Do not apply a tourniquet over a joint (knee or elbow).

Place tourniquet above the injury the loop of the self-adhering band.

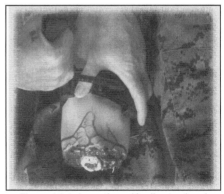

Figure 14-4. Loop the self-adhering band

77

Figure 14-5. Tighten band & secure

Pull the free-running end of the self-adhering band tight and securely fasten it back on itself.

Twist the windlass until the bleeding has stopped.

Figure 14-6. Twist Windlass

Figure 14-7. Lock the rod

Lock the rod in place with the windlass clip.

Pull the free running end of the self-adhering band tight and securely fasten it back on itself. Do not adhere the band past the windlass clip.

Figure 14-8. Secure band

78

Mark the Casualty

If you have to leave the casualty, write the letter "T" and the time the tourniquet was applied on the casualty's forehead with a marker, the casualty's blood, mud, or other substance. The "T" alerts medical personnel that a tourniquet has been applied.

Dressing an Amputation

After the tourniquet has been applied to a complete amputation, place a dressing made of soft, absorbent material over the end of the stump and secure the dressing with bandages. The dressing will help to prevent additional contamination of the wound and will help to protect the wound from additional injury. If the amputation was complete, take care of the amputated part. If possible, rinse the amputated part free of debris, wrap it loosely in saline-moistened sterile gauze, seal the amputated part in a plastic bag or cravat, and place it in a cool container.

Preventing and Controlling Shock

Hypovolemic (low blood volume) shock can result in death. Take measures to prevent or control shock.

Hypovolemic shock is usually caused by severe bleeding, but it can also be caused by a severe loss of body fluids from severe burns, vomiting, diarrhea, and excessive sweating from heat injury.

Signs and symptoms of shock:

- Sweaty but cool (clammy) skin.

- Pale skin.

- Restlessness, nervousness, or agitated behavior.

- Unusual thirst.

- Confused mental process.

- Rapid breathing.

- Blotchy bluish skin, especially around the mouth.

- Nausea.

Measures for Preventing and Controlling Shock

Position the casualty: Position the casualty on his back. If possible, place a jacket or some type of barrier/blanket under the casualty to protect him from the temperature or dampness of the ground. Elevate the casualty's legs so that his feet are slightly higher than the level of his heart. This helps the blood in the veins of his legs to return to his heart. Place a backpack, rolled tactical jacket, or other stable object under the casualty's feet or ankles in order to maintain the elevation. Don't elevate the legs until all lower limb fractures have been splinted.

Exceptions to the Normal Shock Position

Spinal injuries: Keep a casualty with a suspected spinal fracture or a severe head injury as still as possible. Do not elevate the casualty's legs. Immobilize his head, neck, and back, if possible.

Open chest wounds: If the casualty wants to sit up, help him to sit with his back to a wall, tree, or other support. Sitting may help him to breathe easier. If the casualty wants to lie down, position him so that he is lying on his injured side. Lying on his injured side may help to control pain. Also, this permits the uninjured side to breathe easier.

Open abdominal wounds: Keep the casualty on his back with his knees flexed or raised with his feet on the ground. Keeping the knees flexed reduces stress to the abdomen.

Minor head wound: A casualty with a minor head wound should be allowed to sit up. If the casualty has bleeding into the mouth or if he does not want to sit up, position him on his side with his wound up and his head turned so that fluid can drain from his mouth.

Unconsciousness: Position an unconscious casualty on his side with his head turned so fluids can drain from his mouth. If the casualty vomits, quickly perform a finger sweep to clear his airway.

Splint the limb, if appropriate: Splinting the injured limb can reduce additional damage to the limb and help to reduce pain and the risk of shock.

If the casualty is in shock, do not give him anything to eat or drink. If you leave the casualty in order to seek medical help, tell the casualty that you are going to get medical help and will return. Before leaving, turn the casualty's head to one side. This position will help to keep the casualty from choking should he vomit.

Sixteen

Spinal Fracture

Injury to the spine may cause paralysis and even death. Unless an immediate, life-threatening danger is present such as a fire, explosions, an active shooter, etc., you should not move a casualty with a suspected back or neck injury. Immobilize the casualty to prevent movement of his back and neck and seek medical help for the casualty. Treat any casualty, which you think may have a spinal injury, as though you were certain that he had a fractured spine.

Recognize a possible spinal injury:

- Pain or tenderness of the neck or back.

- Cut or bruise on the neck or back.

- Inability to move part of the body (paralysis), especially the legs.

- Lack of feeling in a body part.

- Loss of bladder and/or bowel control.

- Head or back in an unusual position.

Seek medical help and prepare the casualty for evacuation.

These lifesaving skills that we have discussed in all the previous chapters have been gathered from many resources as well as personal experience.

I can't stress enough the importance of seeking out practical hands on training before performing any of the tactics discussed in this book. Certified training is a must when performing these skills.

The Warrior Spirit & the Tactical Lifesaver

A well-prepared officer anticipates that every time he is in contact with another person, whether it's a traffic stop or a larceny report, he may have to engage the "Warrior Spirit" without a moment's notice to survive an encounter that may take his life.

How do we capture that spirit? First, you must always approach every call as if your about to encounter a deadly force situation, no matter what the radio run is. It is most important, however, to treat every citizen, victim, suspect, and witness in a professional manner. Treat them the way you would want to be treated if you were that person, but if the situation goes south, engaging the "Warrior Spirit" needs to be automatic.

Your focus must teeter on that fine edge with every citizen encounter as if you're preparing for a SWAT operation. Your focus needs to be clear and you must have the ability to switch to a fighting mode in a fraction of a second without any hesitation. You must always assume that every citizen contact can become a deadly force encounter and if it does you won't accept failure.

In 1725 a Mohican Chief named Aupumut told his warriors:

When it comes time to die, be not like those whose hearts are filled with the fear of death, so when their time comes, they weep and pray for a little more time to live their lives over again in a different way. Sing your death song, and die like a hero going home.

Chief Aupumut obviously recognized that his Warriors' mindset was the first step in the overall preparation of their development. The point here is that you must accept the fact that someday you may sacrifice your life doing your job, so don't dwell in the possibility. Dwelling on death develops fear and fear develops apprehension. If you're confronted in a combat situation apprehension in the slightest can lead to a slower reaction time. Obviously a slower reaction time gives your adversary an edge.

The "Warrior Spirit" is a combination of confidence, con-centration, and tenacity. Those qualities are worthless without the physical skill and ability to complete the task but so, too, are the physical abilities without the proper mindset.

Here are a few tips to help develop the "Warrior Spirit"

- Be *aware* all the time and *anticipate* a threat.

- Train like you fight.

- Never quit.

- Build confidence through training and fitness.

- Fight chaos with chaos. Use speed, surprise, and violence of action.

- Create the mindset that killing a homicidal adversary is an acceptable action.

Here is a training principle that I like to use when training SWAT officers:

Training should be designed to be uncomfortable, physically and mentally. It should take officers to stressful dark places where they have never gone before, under a controlled environment, so that if they are ever taken there by an adversary it won't be their first time.

An officer's ability to react under duress, pain, and seemingly insurmountable odds remains the hallmark of the "Warrior Spirit." Tenacity against an adversary must be trained, expected, and demanded from your officers.

86

Index

Index